Birthday Surprise
Sorpresa de cumpleaños

by Deborah Schecter

ISBN: 978-1-338-70279-8
Illustrated by Anne Kennedy
Copyright © 2020 by Deborah Schecter. All rights reserved.
Published by Scholastic Inc., 557 Broadway, New York, NY 10012

10 9 8 7 6   68   23 24 25 26/0

Printed in Jiaxing, China. First printing, June 2020.

SCHOLASTIC

I have paper.

Tengo papel.

I have scissors.

Tengo tijeras.

I have ribbon.

Tengo cinta.

I have glue.

Tengo pegamento.

I have stickers.

Tengo pegatinas.

I have crayons.

Tengo crayones.

I have a birthday card for you!

¡Tengo una tarjeta
de cumpleaños para ti!